はしがき

　物事を成就させるためには、その過程こそが大切です。『seek next 英語総合問題 SECOND EDITION』シリーズは、日頃の基礎固めの英語学習から、さらに受験に対応する力までを養成するために編集された総合問題集です。当シリーズは、各学習段階に応じた5冊から成り、「文法」「作文」「リスニング」「速読」「長文読解」を中心とした構成となっています。

　このシリーズの1冊目にあたる本書『seek next 1 SECOND EDITION』は、文法体系に基づく展開で、各レッスンの文法事項を軸として学習を進められるようにしています。各レッスンの「文法」の文法事項が「作文」「長文読解」へと連動しており、文法事項を確実に定着できるように工夫しています。

　また、各レッスンの「リスニング」と「速読」では、「長文読解」と同じテーマや、関連したテーマの英文を収録して、リスニングや掲示、ウェブサイト、広告などのさまざまな読み物を通して、知識を深めることができるようにしています。

本書の構成と特色

各レッスンは4ページ構成で、全部で15レッスンから成っています。各レッスンを「文法」➡「作文」➡「リスニング」➡「速読」➡「長文読解」の流れで構成しました。

■ Grammar
- 必ず習得するべき重要項目を厳選し、文法体系に基づいて15レッスンに配しました。

■ Writing
- 各レッスンの文法事項をふまえた部分整序作文問題もしくは英訳完成問題です。Grammar と連動した問題内容です。

■ Listening
- 各レッスンの「長文読解」と同じテーマの英文を聞き取ります。
- さまざまな試験の形式に対応した問題を収録しています。
- (🔊) は、教師用付属の音声 CD のトラック番号を示します。二次元コードを読み取って、音声をPC やスマートフォンなどから聞くこともできます。

■ Rapid Reading
- 各レッスンの「長文読解」と同じテーマの英文を収録しています。
- ふつうの英文だけでなく、掲示、広告、メールなどの読み取り問題など、さまざまな形式の問題を収録しています。

■ Reading
- 各レッスンの文法事項を含んだ長文読解問題です。興味を引く題材、知的好奇心を喚起する題材、SDGs に対応した題材を選びました。
- 各レッスンの「リスニング」と「速読」と同じテーマの英文を収録しています。
- 速読問題：設定された時間内に本文を読み、本文の要旨や概要についての理解を問う問題としました。
- 精読問題：本文の内容上の重要箇所に関する問題や文法事項を含む問題、本文全体に関する内容把握問題から成ります。

CAN-DO List
- 各レッスンの学習の到達目標を「知識・技能」、「思考力・判断力・表現力」の観点から示しています。満点が取れたら、□にチェックを入れましょう。

Contents

Rapid Reading		Reading		
テーマ	問題形式			
食べ物	共通テスト	生物種の消滅と存続について。	2 ZERO HUNGER / 12 RESPONSIBLE CONSUMPTION AND PRODUCTION	141 words
天体		月の謎について。		178 words
動物	英検®	自分の命をかけた母スズメ。		189 words
買い物	GTEC®	近代的なスーパーマーケットの誕生。	9 INDUSTRY, INNOVATION AND INFRASTRUCTURE	168 words
テクノロジー	GTEC®	仮想ゴーグルが可能にすること。	9 INDUSTRY, INNOVATION AND INFRASTRUCTURE	159 words
生活	英検®	左ききの人を取り巻く環境。		158 words
仕事	英検®	リモート会議の特徴やメリット。	8 DECENT WORK AND ECONOMIC GROWTH	163 words
休暇	共通テスト	日本人と有給休暇。	8 DECENT WORK AND ECONOMIC GROWTH	160 words
環境（水問題）	共通テスト	水質汚染と「死の海域」。	6 CLEAN WATER AND SANITATION / 14 LIFE BELOW WATER	187 words
新聞	英検®	アメリカの新聞について。		171 words
環境	英検®	「もったいない」を唱えたワンガリ・マータイさん。	12 RESPONSIBLE CONSUMPTION AND PRODUCTION	214 words
自転車	英検®	オランダで自転車利用が普及している理由。		201 words
海洋汚染	英検®	プラスチックによる海洋汚染問題。	14 LIFE BELOW WATER / 17 PARTNERSHIPS FOR THE GOALS	168 words
仕事	英検®	テレワークがもたらす利点。	8 DECENT WORK AND ECONOMIC GROWTH	215 words
夜	GTEC®	ニウエの暗い夜空を守る取り組み。	11 SUSTAINABLE CITIES AND COMMUNITIES	194 words

Lesson 1 文の種類①

Grammar　目標 ➡ 7分

1 次の各文を(　　)内の指示にしたがって書きかえなさい。　　　　　(各3点)

1. You are hungry.（疑問文に）

_____

2. I know his phone number.（否定文に）

_____

3. Tom speaks Japanese.（疑問文に）

_____

4. They enjoyed the party yesterday.（否定文に）

_____

2 (　　)内に下記の語群から適語を選んで補いなさい。　　　　　(各2点)

1. (　　　　　　) is your favorite singer?
2. (　　　　　　) is your favorite sport?
3. There are four umbrellas here.　(　　　　　　) is yours?
4. (　　　　　　) do you usually come to school?　―― By bicycle.
5. (　　　　　　) did your family go for vacation last year?
6. (　　　　　　) were you late?　―― I was late because I missed the bus.

　【How / What / Where / Which / Who / Why】

Writing　目標 ➡ 5分

3 (　　)内に与えられた語句を並べかえて、英文を完成しなさい。　　　　　(各4点)

1. アンはサッカーに興味をもっていません。

　Ann (in / interested / is / not / soccer).

_____

2. メグは紅茶は飲みますが、コーヒーは飲みません。

　Meg drinks tea, but (coffee / does / drink / not / she).

_____

3. プールの水の深さはどのくらいありますか。

　How (deep / in / is / the water) the pool?

_____

Listening

目標 ➡ 3分 テーマ 生き物 共通テスト 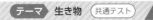 2〜3

4 英語を聞き、それぞれの内容と最もよく合っているものを一つずつ選びなさい。 （各5点）

1. ① The speaker doesn't have a dog now.　② The speaker had a dog in the past.
　③ The speaker has a dog and a cat.　④ The speaker likes neither dogs nor cats.

2. ① Flowers bloomed in the garden last week.
　② The speaker doesn't have to water the plant every day.
　③ The speaker is trying to grow flowers.
　④ There is a bottle of water in the garden.

Rapid Reading

目標 ➡ 5分 テーマ 食べ物 共通テスト

5 メッセージのやりとりを読み取って、問いに対する答えとして最も適当なものを一つずつ選びなさい。 （各5点）

> John, what time can you come home today?

> I'll leave work on time today and I can come straight home.

> Then I'd like to ask you to shop on your way home.　I forgot to buy a salad dressing today.　I'd like the usual Caesar salad dressing — 350 ml.　And don't forget to buy *natto* for breakfast tomorrow.　Make sure it is *natto* that isn't made from *genetically modified soybeans.

> Is it no good otherwise?

> Yeah, check the label carefully!

> OK!　I'll be back as soon as possible.

5 genetically modified：遺伝子組み換えの

1. What was John asked to do?
　① To buy some food.　② To come home early.
　③ To cook breakfast tomorrow.　④ To decide what kind of dressing to buy.

2. What should John be careful about when he buys *natto*?
　① The amount.　② The price.
　③ The soybeans.　④ The taste.

 〈思考力・判断力・表現力〉基本的な情報を聞き取り、把握することができる。
〈思考力・判断力・表現力〉メッセージから、自分が必要とする情報を読み取ることができる。

Lesson 1　5

Reading　目標➡20分　　文法項目　否定文・疑問文　テーマ　生物　　4

速 読問題　次の英文を2.5分で読んで、1．の問いに答えなさい。

　　Over the centuries, farmers have discovered thousands of different *species of food

*crops.　(1)Each species has special qualities.　Some can be grown in very hot or cold

climates.　Others are not affected by certain diseases.　However, you won't find many

of (2)these species in your local supermarket.　To feed the seven billion people on Earth,

5　most farmers today are growing only species of plants and farming only species of

animals that are easy to (3)produce in large numbers.　*Meanwhile, thousands of other

species are becoming *extinct.

　　For example, in the Philippines, there were once thousands of varieties of rice ; now

fewer than 100 are grown (4)there.　In China, 90 percent of the wheat varieties grown

10　just a century ago have disappeared.　Experts believe that over the past century, we

have allowed more than half of the world's food varieties to (5)disappear.　　(141 words)

---

¹ species [spíːʃiːz]：(動植物の)種　² crop [krɑ́(ː)p]：穀物　⁶ meanwhile [míːn(h)wàɪl]：一方
⁷ extinct [ɪkstíŋ(k)t]：絶滅した

CAN-DO List　☐ 〈知識・技能〉否定文、疑問文について理解できる。
　　　　　　　☐ 〈思考力・判断力・表現力〉生物種の消滅について的確に理解できる。

1. この英文で主に述べられているものを、次の a.～ d.から選びなさい。　　　　　（ 5 点）

　　a. 食料としての穀物種について

　　b. 食料の大量生産について

　　c. スーパーマーケットで売られる穀物について

　　d. 絶滅危惧種の保存について

精 **読問題** もう一度英文を読んで、次の問いに答えなさい。

2. **文法** 下線部(1)に関連して、(ア)：「この植物には特別な性質がない。」という否定文と、(イ)：「この植物には特別な性質がありますか。」という疑問文になるように、次の文の空所に適語を補いなさい。　　　　　（各 3 点）

　　(ア) This plant (　　　　　　　) (　　　　　　　　　) any special qualities.

　　(イ) (　　　　　　　　　) this plant (　　　　　　　　) any special qualities?

3. 下線部(2)は、何の種のことですか。本文中から 2 語で抜き出しなさい。　　　　（ 5 点）

　　(　　　　　　　) (　　　　　　　　)

4. 下線部(3)をわかりやすい日本語（漢字 4 字）で表しなさい。　　　　　　　　　（ 6 点）

5. 下線部(4)は具体的にはどこのことですか。本文中から 2 語で抜き出しなさい。　　（ 6 点）

　　in (　　　　　　　) (　　　　　　　　)

6. 下線部(5)とほぼ同じ意味になるように、空所に入る適語を本文中から抜き出しなさい。　（ 6 点）

　　become (　　　　　　　　)

7. **全体把握** 本文の内容と合っているものにはＴ、合っていないものにはＦと答えなさい。（各 2 点）

　　(ア) All species of food crops can be grown in very hot or cold climates.　(　　　　　)

　　(イ) We can find thousands of different species in our local supermarket.　(　　　　　)

　　(ウ) There are about seven billion people in the world.　　　　　　　　　(　　　　　)

　　(エ) There are thousands of varieties of rice in the Philippines now.　　　(　　　　　)

　　(オ) China grows 90 percent of all the wheat in the world.　　　　　　　(　　　　　)

Grammar 目標 ➡ 7分

1 例にならって、次の疑問文を（　　）内の表現に続けなさい。 （各3点）

例：Where does Susan live? （Do you know ...?）

　→Do you know where Susan lives?

1. What is her telephone number? （I don't know ...）

_____

2. How old is she? （Do you know ...?）

_____

3. Why is she so angry? （I don't know ...）

_____

4. Where did she buy that T-shirt? （I want to know ...）

_____

2 次の各文がほぼ同じ意味になるように、（　　）内に適語を補いなさい。 （各2点）

1. You must study harder. / (　　　　　　　) harder.
2. You must not be late. / (　　　　　　) be late.
3. She is a very nice person. / (　　　　　　) a nice person she is!
4. Her hair is very beautiful. / (　　　　　　) beautiful her hair is!

Writing 目標 ➡ 5分

3 （　　）内に与えられた語句を並べかえて、英文を完成しなさい。 （各4点）

1. なぜあなたがそんなに怒っているのか、私には理解できません。

I don't understand (angry / are / so / why / you).

_____

2. ミルクは冷蔵庫に、アイスクリームは冷凍室に入れなさい。

Put (and / in / the ice cream / the milk / the refrigerator) in the freezer.

_____

3. まあなんて奇妙な服を、彼は着ているのでしょう。

(clothes / he / is / strange / what) wearing!

_____

CAN-DO List ☐ 🔍 〈知識・技能〉間接疑問文、命令文、感嘆文を適切に活用することができる。

4 それぞれのイラストについて対話を聞き、最後の発言に対する相手の応答として最も適当なものを一つずつ選びなさい。 (各5点)

1.

① More than 10 billion.
② Around 2 o'clock.
③ All around a year.
④ In the east sky.

2.

① About 10, in an hour.
② In the east.
③ From 10 p.m. until midnight.
④ You should make a wish.

Rapid Reading 目標 → 5分 　テーマ 天体

5 掲示を読み取って、問いに対する答えとして最も適当なものを一つずつ選びなさい。 (各5点)

---

30 September, 10 a.m.-noon
Discovering Space
Coin Street Neighborhood Center, 108 Stamford Street,
South Bank, SE 1 9NH, London

This workshop will teach you about the exciting latest studies in space.　Learn about why the Sun is so important.　After the workshop, you can stay and watch the movie, "Project Astronomy."

> **Discovering Space**
> ・Spend time in small groups discussing new space studies.
> ・Connect with others interested in learning about space.
> *Register online from **www.space.link.org**

---

10 register [rédʒɪstər]：…を登録する

1. What is the poster about?
   ① How to teach about space.
   ② Learning about how to run a workshop.
   ③ Learning about space.
   ④ Learning about teaching.

2. How can you join the workshop?
   ① Ask a friend.　② Go to London.　③ Go to space.　④ Register online.

速 読問題 次の英文を2.5分で読んで、1. の問いに答えなさい。

For thousands of years, people have looked at the moon. They did not know what the moon was made of. They wanted to know (1)how big it was and how far away it was.

One of the most interesting questions was, "Where did the moon come from?" No one knew the answer. Scientists had many different ideas, but they could not *prove

5 that their ideas were right.

Between 1969 and 1972, the United States sent *astronauts to the moon. They studied the moon and brought some pieces of moon rock back to the earth. Scientists have studied (2)them. Now they can finally answer (3)the question about the birth of the moon.

Today most scientists believe that (4)the moon was born from the earth. They think

10 that a large *object hit the earth early in its history. Perhaps the object was as big as *Mars. When the object hit the earth, very big pieces of the earth broke off. These pieces went into *orbit around the earth. After a short time, the pieces came together and became the moon.

(178 words)

---

4 prove [prúːv]：…を証明する　　6 astronaut [ǽstrənɔ̀ːt]：宇宙飛行士　　10 object [á(ː)bdʒekt]：物体
11 Mars [máːrz]：火星　　12 orbit [ɔ́ːrbət]：軌道

CAN-DO List
□ 〈知識・技能〉間接疑問文について理解できる。
□ 〈思考力・判断力・表現力〉月の誕生について的確に理解できる。

1. この英文で主に述べられているものを、次の a.～d. から選びなさい。　　　　　　（6点）

    a．How big is the moon?

    b．How far away is the moon?

    c．What is the moon made of?

    d．Where did the moon come from?

精 読問題 もう一度英文を読んで、次の問いに答えなさい。

2. 文法 下記の語句を並べかえて、下線部(1)をふつうの疑問文に書きかえなさい。　　（6点）

How big (and / far away / how / it / it / was / was)?

3. 下線部(2)の them は何を指していますか。英語で答えなさい。　　　　　　　　　（7点）

4. 下線部(3)とほぼ同じ内容を表している文を本文中から抜き出しなさい。　　　　　（7点）

5. 下線部(4)の説を、50字程度の日本語で説明しなさい。　　　　　　　　　　　　（10点）

50

6. 全体把握 本文の内容と合っているものにはＴ、合っていないものにはＦと答えなさい。（各2点）

  (ア)　大昔から月は人々にとって身近な天体であり、人々は月を好奇心の対象とすることはなかった。

                                   （　　　　　）

  (イ)　月について最もおもしろい問いは、月はなぜ地球から離れていかないのかであった。

                                   （　　　　　）

  (ウ)　科学者たちは月の誕生についてさまざまな説を唱えたが、その正しさを証明することはできな

     かった。　　　　　　　　　　　　　　　　　　　　　　　　　　　（　　　　　）

  (エ)　現在の科学者たちにとって、月の誕生を考える際の重要な手がかりは宇宙飛行士たちが持ち帰

     った月の石である。　　　　　　　　　　　　　　　　　　　　　　（　　　　　）

  (オ)　月は、地球と同時に生まれた。　　　　　　　　　　　　　　　　　（　　　　　）

  (カ)　月は、創成期の地球に火星が衝突して生まれた。　　　　　　　　　（　　　　　）

Grammar 目標 ➡ 7分

1 ( )内に、右の a.～d. から適当なものを選び、記号を補いなさい。 （各2点）

1. Babies ( ).
2. Jimmy and his dog were ( ).
3. Children usually like ( ).
4. I promise ( ).

   a. chocolate
   b. grow quickly in their first year
   c. good friends
   d. that I'll do my best

2 例にならって、( )内の動詞を用いて書きかえなさい。 （各4点）

例：The small restaurant <u>was</u> famous among tourists. （become）

  →The small restaurant became famous among tourists.

1. She <u>was</u> tired after the race. （look）

_____

2. It <u>is</u> very cold at night. （get）

_____

3. She <u>was</u> sad when he left. （feel）

_____

4. The food in that restaurant <u>is</u> good. （taste）

_____

Writing 目標 ➡ 3分

3 ( )内に適語を補って、英文を完成しなさい。 （各2点）

1. 私は歩いて学校へ通っています。

  I ( ) to school.

2. 兄とぼくはテニスが得意です。

  My brother and I ( ) good tennis players.

3. 眠そうだね。もう寝たらどう？

  You ( ) sleepy. Why don't you ( ) to bed?

4. ロンドンにはよいレストランがたくさんあります。

  London ( ) a lot of good restaurants.

5. 私たちはその先生が京都の出身だと知っています。

  We ( ) that the teacher is from Kyoto.

CAN-DO List ☐ 🔍 〈知識・技能〉第1～第3文型の文を適切に活用することができる。

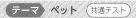
4 英文を聞き、空欄 1 〜 4 に入れるのに最も適当なものを一つずつ選びなさい。   (完答10点)

Japan	1st	1	2nd	2	3rd	Daxhund
America	1st	3	2nd	4	3rd	Golden Retriever
France	1st	Shepherd	2nd	Belgian Malinois	3rd	Golden Retriever

① Chihuahua   ② Labrador Retriever   ③ Shepherd   ④ Toy Poodle

Rapid Reading 目標 ➡ 5分   テーマ 動物 英検®

5 (1)・(2)に入れるのに最も適当なものを一つずつ選びなさい。   (各5点)

It is natural to want to help a baby bird that is alone on the ground.   You think the bird has fallen out of its *nest and may be attacked by other hungry animals.   (1   ), the bird may be in training.   Its mother may be *nearby to show it how to fly.   *Therefore, (2   ).

²nest [nést]：巣   ³nearby [níərbái]：近くに   ³therefore [ðéərfɔːr]：それゆえに

1. ① Because of this
   ② For example
   ③ However
   ④ If so

2. ① if you don't pick up the baby bird, it will be attacked by a hungry animal
   ② if you hear birdsong, you should pick up the baby bird and run away
   ③ taking the baby bird home to raise as a pet will save its life
   ④ you should stand away from the baby bird to see if the mother appears

Reading 目標 ➡ 20分 　　　　　　文法項目 文型 テーマ 動物 ◀)) 9

速 読問題 次の英文を2.5分で読んで、1. の問いに答えなさい。

One day I was walking with my dog on a mountain.　It was a fine day, and I felt good.

My dog was running here and there around me.　Suddenly he stopped and began to

move very carefully.　When I looked toward him, I saw a baby *sparrow behind a tree.

It was so young that it couldn't yet move.　My dog was going to catch it.　(1)Just then

5　the mother sparrow cried out, came down from the tree, and flew just under the dog's

nose.　(2)She wanted to help her baby.　She did not think about herself.　To the

sparrow the dog was a monster.　(3)How large the dog looked to the sparrow!

The mother sparrow was not afraid of anything, so she was able to fly down from

the tree to the dog.　Then my dog stopped moving, and watched the bird for a

10　while.　(4)Soon he began to move back.　He felt that the sparrow was not afraid at all.

I was impressed by how brave the mother bird was.　I knew she loved her baby

deeply.　(5)I called my dog back and left the place.　　　　　　　　　(189 words)

³ sparrow [spǽrou]：スズメ

CAN-DO List ☐ 🔍 〈知識・技能〉第2文型について理解できる。
☐ 💡 〈思考力・判断力・表現力〉動物の親子の愛情について的確に理解できる。

	Grammar	Writing	Listening	Rapid Reading	Reading	Total
	/24	/10	/10	/10	/46	/100

1. この英文で主に述べられているものを、次の a.〜d. から選びなさい。 （5点）

    a. Walking with my dog.

    b. The dog was a monster.

    c. How nice my dog was to the bird!

    d. How brave the mother bird was!

精 読問題 もう一度英文を読んで、次の問いに答えなさい。

2. 下線部(1)の具体的な内容を、日本語で説明しなさい。 （7点）

_____

3. 下線部(2)の具体的な内容を、本文中から３語で抜き出しなさい。 （4点）

_____

4. **文法** 下線部(3)とほぼ同じ意味になるように、次の文の空所に適語を補いなさい。 （4点）

The dog (   ) very (   ) to the sparrow.

5. 下線部(4)について、次の問いに英語で答えなさい。 （7点）

Why did he begin to move back?

_____

6. 下線部(5)の理由を、日本語で説明しなさい。 （7点）

_____

7. **全体把握** 本文の内容と合っているものにはＴ、合っていないものにはＦと答えなさい。 （各2点）

    (ア) When I saw a baby sparrow on the ground, my dog began to bark. (   )

    (イ) The mother sparrow flew down in front of the dog without thinking about herself.

                                                                     (   )

    (ウ) I was sorry that my dog killed the birds. (   )

    (エ) The mother sparrow was afraid of the dog because it was so big. (   )

    (オ) As soon as the mother sparrow came down from the tree, I called my dog back.

                                                                        (   )

    (カ) The mother sparrow's deep love saved the baby sparrow. (   )

Grammar 目標 ➡ 7分

1 次の各文を、Ｓ＋Ｖ＋人＋もの（人にものを～する）の文に書きかえなさい。 （各4点）

1. I gave a present to her.

   _____

2. I lent some money to John.

   _____

3. Ann showed her vacation photos to her friends.

   _____

2 例にならって、次の各文の内容を（　　）内の表現に続けなさい。 （各4点）

例：He was a hero. （Everybody called …）

　　→Everybody called him a hero.

1. Mary was very angry. （Tom's words made …）

   _____

2. His bicycle is clean. （Tom always keeps …）

   _____

3. His bicycle is dirty. （Bob leaves …）

   _____

Writing 目標 ➡ 5分

3 （　　）内に与えられた語句を並べかえて、英文を完成しなさい。 （各4点）

1. お父さんは誕生日のお祝いにぼくに子イヌをくれました。

   My father (a young dog / gave / for / me / my birthday).

   _____

2. メグは私に医者に診てもらうべきだと言いました。

   Meg (I / me / should / that / told) see the doctor.

   _____

3. とても眠くて、私は目を開けておくことができませんでした。

   I was so sleepy that (couldn't / I / keep / my eyes / open).

   _____

CAN-DO List □ 〈知識・技能〉第4、第5文型の文を適切に活用することができる。

Listening

目標 ➡ 3分　　　　テーマ 買い物　GTEC®　🔊 10〜11

4 それぞれの問いについて対話を聞き、答えとして最も適当なものを一つずつ選びなさい。（各5点）

1. 女性は今何を探していますか。

2. 男性は車でどこに向かいますか。

Rapid Reading

目標 ➡ 5分　　　　テーマ 買い物　GTEC®

5 広告を読み取って、問いに対する答えとして最も適当なものを一つずつ選びなさい。　（各5点）

Upcoming 10th Anniversary Sale

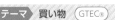

　To celebrate the Anniversary, we'll have a sale starting on Friday, October 31.　The sale will last two weeks.　Don't miss a great chance to get our high-quality glasses.　The following are examples of our bargains.

> Imported brand-name glass frames plus super-thin lenses
> 　　→ Discounted to $185.50
> Light-weight frames for sports
> 　　→ Discounted to $150.50〔lenses not included〕
> Lens exchange to the latest model
> 　　→ Discount 40% from our regular price, $120.00

Joy Sandra's eyewear shop

---

1. How long will the sale continue?

　① Beginning at the end of October.　② For the last two weeks of November.

　③ Until next Friday.　④ Until November 13.

2. What can you buy for $185.50?

　① A pair of glasses for athletes.　② A pair of lenses with a foreign frame.

　③ Imported frames without lenses.　④ Imported high-quality lenses.

Reading　目標➡20分 ／／／／／／／　文法項目 文型　テーマ ビジネス　🔊 12

速読問題 次の英文を2.5分で読んで、1. の問いに答えなさい。

A new *retail concept was introduced in the United States when the first self-service *grocery store, named Piggly Wiggly, opened in 1916. (1)Before that, customers used to bring a shopping list to a neighborhood store and wait while a store clerk collected the items they wanted and measured out products like *flour and rice from large

5　containers. (2)On the other hand, Piggly Wiggly gave customers baskets and asked them to serve themselves. They filled their baskets with packets of flour and rice, cans of vegetables, and other groceries from the store's shelves.

(3)Sales at Piggly Wiggly were higher than at other stores, because customers typically bought more when they *made their own selections. Soon Piggly Wiggly

10　expanded to become a chain of stores, and other (4)markets copied the self-service model. The modern supermarket was born.

It influenced not only the way people shopped but also (5)other *aspects of the food business. For example, food manufacturers started using more attractive packaging in order to draw customers to their products.　　　　　　　　　　　(168 words)

---

¹ retail [ríːtèɪl]：小売りの　² grocery store：食料品店　⁴ flour [fláʊər]：小麦粉
⁹ make a selection：選ぶ　¹² aspect [æspekt]：側面

CAN-DO List　☐ 🔍 〈知識・技能〉第4文型、第5文型について理解できる。
　　　　　　　☐ 💡 〈思考力・判断力・表現力〉近代的なスーパーマーケットの誕生について的確に理解できる。

1. この英文のタイトルとして最も適当なものを、次の a.～ d.から選びなさい。 （5点）

    a. The Attractive Way of Shopping in the U.S.

    b. The Birth of the Modern Retail Shop

    c. The Great Change in the Food Industry

    d. The Source of the Piggly Wiggly

精 読問題 もう一度英文を読んで、次の問いに答えなさい。

2. 下線部(1)は具体的にいつのことですか。日本語で説明しなさい。 （6点）

3. 文法 下線部(2)について、Piggly Wiggly は従来の食料品店とどう違いましたか。日本語で説明しなさい。 （7点）

4. 下線部(3)について、Piggly Wiggly の売り上げが伸びたのはなぜですか。日本語で説明しなさい。 （7点）

5. 下線部(4)の語に最も近い意味の語句を、次の a.～ d.から選びなさい。 （4点）

    a. customers   b. economic system

    c. food manufacturers   d. grocery stores

6. 下線部(5)の例を、本文中から 1 語で抜き出しなさい。 （5点）

    (　　　　　　　　)

7. 全体把握 本文の内容と合っているものにはＴ、合っていないものにはＦと答えなさい。 （各2点）

    (ア) Piggly Wiggly was the name of a self-service restaurant.   (　　　　)

    (イ) Customers didn't have to take a shopping list to Piggly Wiggly.   (　　　　)

    (ウ) A store clerk wrote a list for customers until 1916.   (　　　　)

    (エ) At Piggly Wiggly, customers measured rice by themselves.   (　　　　)

    (オ) Food manufacturers changed the way of packaging food.   (　　　　)

Lesson 5 時制①

Grammar　目標 ➡ 7分

1 次の各文の（　　　）内に入れるのに最も適当なものを選び、記号を補いなさい。　（各2点）

1. I (　　　　) hungry.　Can I have something to eat?

   a. am　　　　　　b. was　　　　　　c. will be

2. When I was a child, I (　　　　) to be a firefighter.

   a. want　　　　　　b. wanted　　　　　　c. will want

3. Goodbye.　I (　　　　) you tomorrow, OK?

   a. call　　　　　　b. called　　　　　　c. will call

4. What (　　　　) to the party tomorrow?

   a. are you going to wear　　　b. do you wear　　　c. did you wear

2 次の各文の（　　　）内から適当なほうを選びなさい。　（各2点）

1. In Japan, it (rains / is raining) a lot in June.

2. Take an umbrella with you.　It (rains / is raining).

3. Where's Tom?——He (takes / is taking) a shower.

4. Tom (takes / is taking) a shower every morning.

5. Linda (read / was reading) a book when the telephone (rang / was ringing).

6. Mary (broke / was breaking) her leg while she (skated / was skating).

Writing　目標 ➡ 5分

3 （　　　）内に与えられた語句を並べかえて、英文を完成しなさい。　（各4点）

1. 今夜は、イタリア料理の店で夕食をとります。

   We (are / dinner / going / have / to) at an Italian restaurant tonight.

   _____

2. 「すみませんが、そこは私の席なのですが。」「おや、ごめんなさい。」

   Excuse me, (are / in / my place / sitting / you).——Oh, I'm sorry.

   _____

3. 私が起きたときは、雨は降っていませんでした。

   It (got / I / raining / wasn't / when) up.

   _____

CAN-DO List　□　〈知識・技能〉現在（進行）形、過去（進行）形、未来表現の文を適切に活用することができる。

4 対話とそれについての問いを聞き、その答えとして最も適当なものを一つずつ選びなさい。

(各5点)

1. 旅行中の夫婦が話をしています。

2. 男性が商品について店員に尋ねています。

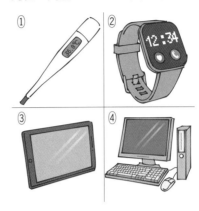

Rapid Reading 目標 ➡ 5分 　テーマ テクノロジー （GTEC®）

5 広告を読み取って、問いに対する答えとして最も適当なものを一つずつ選びなさい。 (各5点)

Which smartphone should you choose?
Here are 4 types of smartphones that are easy to buy.

Model	Manufacturer	Generation	Features	Price (Tax Included)
A-41	A Mobile	4G	· Simple and safe design · Long lasting battery	¥20,000
A-51	A Mobile	5G	· Most recent model · Latest, most advanced technology	¥150,000
B-41	B Mobile	4G	· Long lasting high quality · Choice of various colors	¥30,000
B-51	B Mobile	5G	· Latest 5G model · Thinnest in the world (about 7 mm)	¥160,000

If you buy within this month, we'll sell all products at a 10% discount.

Daiichi electronics store

1. If you wish to buy the latest model of a cheap smartphone, which model would you buy?

① A-41 　　② A-51 　　③ B-41 　　④ B-51

2. If you buy B-41 this month, how much will you pay?

① ¥27,000 　　② ¥28,000 　　③ ¥30,000 　　④ ¥33,000

Reading 目標 ➡ 20分 | 文法項目 現在形・過去形・未来表現 | テーマ 情報・通信 | 15

速 読問題 次の英文を2.5分で読んで、1. の問いに答えなさい。

Smartphones, tablets, and laptops are getting *thinner and lighter than ever before. However, in the future, you might not need to carry any (1)*gadgets* around with you. If designers *have their way, you may just need to wear a pair of "virtual goggles" instead. (2)Scientists are testing *prototypes at the moment, (3)though it may be some

5 time before (4)they're actually on store shelves.

These goggles will act like a computer screen and display information and entertainment from the Internet. So, (5)when you are sightseeing, you'll be able to see information about a famous building in front of you. Or you'll be able to get a *review of the restaurant menu you're looking at. The goggles will have GPS, so you'll be able

10 to *stream directions to a party or *locate a nearby coffee shop. They will also have a camera to take photos, and you won't need a cell phone anymore. The goggles will have that built in, too.

(159 words)

---

¹ thin [θín]：細い　　²gadget [gǽdʒɪt]：道具、装置　　³have one's way：思い通りにする
⁴prototype [próʊtətàɪp]：原型、試作品　　⁸review [rɪvjúː]：批評、評価
¹⁰stream [stríːm]：…を同時再生する　　¹⁰locate [lóʊkeɪt]：…を突き止める、探し出す

  □ 〈知識・技能〉現在(進行)形・過去(進行)形・未来表現について理解できる。
□ 〈思考力・判断力・表現力〉仮想ゴーグルについて的確に理解できる。

1. この英文のタイトルとして最も適当なものを、次のa.～d.から選びなさい。 (5点)

    a. Future Smartphones

    b. Gadgets

    c. Prototypes

    d. Virtual Goggles

精 読問題 もう一度英文を読んで、次の問いに答えなさい。

2. 下線部(1)は具体的に何のことですか。本文中の英語で答えなさい。 (6点)

3. 文法 下線部(2)に関連して、「科学者はそのとき試作品をテストしていました。」という過去の文になるように、次の文の空所に適語を補いなさい。 (5点)

Scientists (   ) (   ) prototypes at that moment.

4. 下線部(3)の though に最も近い意味を、次のa.～d.から選びなさい。 (4点)

    a. もっとも…だが   b. …であるのに対して

    c. …にもかかわらず   d. たとえ…(する)にしても

5. 下線部(4)の they は何を指していますか。本文中の英語で答えなさい。 (6点)

6. 下線部(5)について、観光しているときに virtual goggles があればどのようなことが可能になりますか。日本語で2つ答えなさい。 (各6点)

7. 全体把握 本文の内容と合っているものにはT、合っていないものにはFと答えなさい。 (各2点)

    (ア) Smartphones, tablets, and laptops are getting thicker and heavier than ever before. (   )

    (イ) "Virtual goggles" are now sold in stores. (   )

    (ウ) "Virtual goggles" are a device that we wear, not carry. (   )

    (エ) "Virtual goggles" work like a computer. (   )

    (オ) If we have "virtual goggles," we won't need a cell phone. (   )

Grammar 目標 ➡ 7分

1 ( )内に下記の語群から適語を選び、過去分詞にして補いなさい。 (各2点)

1. John, this is Mary. ── Yes, I know. We've already ( ).

2. Is Paul here? ── No, he hasn't ( ) yet.

3. Bob is on vacation. ── Oh, where has he ( )?

4. I've seen that girl, but I've never ( ) to her.

5. Have you ever ( ) to Hawaii? ── Yes, twice.

【arrive / be / go / meet / speak】

2 ( )内の語句を付け加えて、現在完了形の文を作りなさい。 (各3点)

1. I am in the hospital. (since Monday)

_____

2. My brother has a cold. (for two weeks)

_____

3. I know Amy. (for a long time)

_____

Writing 目標 ➡ 5分

3 ( )内に適語を補って、英文を完成しなさい。 (各3点)

1. 彼は夏休みの計画をもう立てています。

He has ( ) ( ) his plans for the summer vacation.

2. 私はめがねを持たないで学校に来てしまいました。

I've ( ) to school ( ) my glasses.

3. 私は馬に乗ったことは一度もありません。

I've ( ) ( ) a horse.

4. 日記をつけようとしたことがありますか。

Have you ever ( ) to ( ) a diary?

5. 彼は35年間医者をしていて、経験が豊富です。

He has ( ) a doctor for 35 years, and has a lot of experience.

6. 私はけさからずっとその本を読んでいます。

I have ( ) ( ) the book since this morning.

CAN-DO List □ 〈知識・技能〉現在完了形、現在完了進行形の文を適切に活用することができる。

Listening

目標 → 3分　　　　　　　　テーマ 生活　🔊 16〜17

4 英語の質問と、それに対する応答が4つ読まれます。応答として最も適当なものを一つずつ選びなさい。 (各5点)

1. ①　②　③　④
2. ①　②　③　④

Rapid Reading

目標 → 5分　　　　　　　　テーマ 生活　英検®

5 (1)・(2)に入れるのに最も適当なものを一つずつ選びなさい。 (各5点)

　Children who are left-handed have more accidents than right-handed children. Doctors have two *theories to explain this fact. One theory says that left-handed children may simply fall and *bump into things more. The other theory, (　1　), explains the accidents very differently. *According to this theory, the problem is not with the children, but with the world around them. Most things, such as doors, cars, and toys (　2　).

> ²theory [θíːəri]：説、理論　　³bump [bʌ́mp]：(ドシンと)ぶつかる　　⁴according to ...：…によれば

1. ① for example
   ② however
   ③ in fact
   ④ therefore
2. ① are designed and used best by right-handed people
   ② are designed for left-handed people
   ③ are made by people without children
   ④ are not designed for right-handed people

Reading
目標 ➡ 20分　　　　文法項目 現在完了形　テーマ 生活　 18

速読問題 次の英文を2.5分で読んで、1．の問いに答えなさい。

Since the beginning of time, some people (the right-handed ones) have believed that there is something wrong with (1)left-handers.　Right-handed people have thought that left-handers are strange.　However, if you are left-handed, there's no need to feel lonely.　About a tenth of the world's *population is left-handed, and *unfair attitudes

5　against "lefties" are changing.　(2)Most parents *no longer *force children to use their right hand if they really like to use their left.

　　The right-handers of the world have begun to realize (3)how unfair the world has been to its left-handed members.　For a left-hander, *scissors won't cut; can-openers won't work; cars are difficult to drive.　But at last, help has come for the "lefties."　(4)*Anything

10　*Left-Handed* is a new shop in London.　It sells, at low prices, good *products made for left-handed people.　This shop has everything from left-handed scissors to left-handed can-openers, pens and golf clubs.　The owner of *Anything Left-Handed*, *by the way, is right-handed.

(158 words)

---

⁴population [pὰ(:)pjəléɪʃ(ə)n]：人口　　⁴unfair attitudes：不公平な態度　　⁵no longer ...：もはや…ない
⁵force [fɔ́ːrs]：…に～することを強制する　　⁸scissors [sízərz]：はさみ　　¹⁰product [prά(:)dʌkt]：製品
¹²by the way：(話題を切りかえて)ところで

CAN-DO List　☐ 〈知識・技能〉現在完了形(継続)について理解できる。
☐ 〈思考力・判断力・表現力〉左ききの人の不便さの解消について的確に理解できる。

	Grammar	Writing	Listening	Rapid Reading	Reading	Total
	/19	/18	/10	/10	/43	/100

1. この英文で主に述べられているものを、次の a.～ d. から選びなさい。 （5点）

a. 左ききの人々に対する根強い偏見。

b. 消えつつある、左ききの人々に対する偏見。

c. 左ききの人々が味わう生活の不便。

d. 左ききの人々のための専門店の出現。

精 読問題 もう一度英文を読んで、次の問いに答えなさい。

2. 下線部(1)とほぼ同じ内容を表している 1 語を本文中から抜き出しなさい。 （4点）

（　　　　　　　　　）

3. 下線部(2)から、かつてはほとんどの親たちはどういうことをしていたとわかりますか。日本語で説明しなさい。 （8点）

_____

_____

4. **文法** 下線部(3)について、具体例を日本語で 3 つ箇条書きしなさい。 （各2点）

_____

_____

_____

5. 下線部(4)はどんな店ですか。日本語で簡潔に説明しなさい。 （8点）

_____

6. **全体把握** 本文の内容と合っているものには T、合っていないものには F と答えなさい。 （各2点）

(ア) There is something wrong with left-handers. （　　　　　）

(イ) About 10% of the people in the world are left-handed. （　　　　　）

(ウ) It is difficult for right-handed people to drive cars. （　　　　　）

(エ) *Anything Left-Handed* sells left-handed golf clubs. （　　　　　）

(オ) The products in the shop are expensive. （　　　　　）

(カ) The shop's owner is left-handed. （　　　　　）

Grammar 目標➡7分

1 次の各文の（　）内に、can、may、must から適語を選んで補いなさい。　（各2点）

1. She is over eighty, but she (　　　　　　) read without glasses.

2. (　　　　　　) I ask a question?

3. All students (　　　　　) keep quiet in the library.

4. Take an umbrella with you. It (　　　　　) rain.

2 次の各文の（　）内に入れるのに最も適当なものを選び、記号を補いなさい。　（各2点）

1. Have you seen my keys? I (　　　　　) find them.

   a. can't　　　　　b. may not　　　　c. must not

2. You (　　　　) be late for school again!

   a. don't have to　　b. have to　　　　c. must　　　　d. must not

3. It's a very good book. You (　　　　) read it.

   a. can　　　　　b. may　　　　　c. should

4. You watch TV all the time. You (　　　　　) watch TV so much.

   a. don't　　　　b. may not　　　　c. should not

Writing 目標➡5分

3 （　）内に与えられた語を並べかえて、英文を完成しなさい。　（各4点）

1. イルカは話すことができると言う人もいる。

   Some people (can / dolphins / say / talk / that).

   _____

2. このことはだれにも話してはいけません。秘密なのですから。

   You (about / anyone / mustn't / tell / this). It's a secret.

   _____

3. ブラウン先生、先生について質問してもいいでしょうか。

   Ms. Brown, may (about / ask / I / you / yourself)?

   _____

4. 私は彼に電話をしたほうがいいと思いますか。

   Do you (I / him / phone / should / think)?

   _____

CAN-DO List ☐ 🔍 〈知識・技能〉助動詞を使った文を適切に活用することができる。

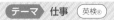
4 対話と質問を聞き、その答えとして最も適当なものを一つずつ選びなさい。 (各5点)

1. ① Attend a meeting.　　② Take an exam.
　 ③ Participate in a game.　④ Go to a class.

2. ① Attend a meeting in Osaka.　② Attend an online meeting.
　 ③ Be absent from a meeting.　　④ Go on a business trip.

5 案内を読み取って、問いに対する答えとして最も適当なものを一つずつ選びなさい。 (各5点)

To the people concerned

1st Business Meeting

We will hold a meeting on new drinks which will go on sale this spring, as follows :

1. Date and time : June 3 (Tue.), from 10:00

2. Place : Meeting Room 302

3. What to bring : Printed documents about new drinks that have already been delivered

Note : Each participant will be asked to think about a sales strategy for selling new drinks and make a presentation on that day.

Sales manager

---

1. When will participants get the documents?

　① No documents will be given.

　② They have already been given.

　③ They will be given by the day before the meeting.

　④ They will be given on the day of the meeting.

2. What are participants required to do at the meeting?

　① To give a presentation on a sales strategy.

　② To have a discussion on new drinks.

　③ To only attend the meeting.

　④ To read the documents in advance.

Reading　目標 ➡20分　文法項目 can の用法　テーマ 情報・通信　 21

速 読問題 次の英文を2.5分で読んで、1. の問いに答えなさい。

What is a "*remote meeting"?　It is almost the same as a "virtual meeting" or an "online meeting."　In any type of meeting, such as *face-to-face or remote, people get together to *present ideas and make decisions.　It (1)can be a meeting to get something done.

The difference between a real face-to-face meeting and a remote meeting is that

5 *participants of the remote meeting are just not in the same *physical space. Instead, (2)they are connected by phones or the Internet.　There are several types of remote (3)sessions.　Among them, the group call is widely used because it is *handy.　(4)This type of remote meeting does not require any extra *equipment other than a cellphone or computer.　It can be a video call, with each participant seeing all

10 the others, or just *audio.

It is easy to *participate in, but (5)to have an *efficient meeting, the number of participants should be limited.　*Ideally, there should be *at most ten participants in the group call.

(163 words)

---

¹remote [rɪmóʊt]：遠隔の　　²face-to-face：対面の、面と向かっての
³present [prɪzént]：…を提案する、口頭発表する　　⁵participant [pərtísɪp(ə)nt]：参加者
⁵physical [fízɪk(ə)l]：物理的な、実際の　　⁸handy [hǽndi]：便利な　　⁸equipment [ɪkwípmənt]：機器
¹⁰audio [ɔ́:diòʊ]：音声の　　¹¹participate in ...：…に参加する　　¹¹efficient [ɪfíʃ(ə)nt]：能率的な
¹²ideally [aɪdí:(ə)li]：理想を言えば　　¹²at most：多くて、せいぜい

| CAN-DO List | ☐ 🔍 〈知識・技能〉can の用法について理解できる。 |
| | ☐ 💭 〈思考力・判断力・表現力〉リモート会議の特徴について的確に理解できる。 |

1. この英文のタイトルとして最も適当なものを、次の a.〜d. から選びなさい。　　　　（5点）

   a. A Face-to-face Meeting

   b. A Remote Meeting

   c. A Video Call

   d. An Efficient Meeting

精 読問題 もう一度英文を読んで、次の問いに答えなさい。

2. **文法** 下線部(1)の can の意味として最も適当なものを、次の a.〜d. から選びなさい。　（5点）

   a. ときに〜することがある　　　　　　　b. 〜できる

   c. …が(見えて)いる　　　　　　　　　　d. 〜してもよい

3. 下線部(2)の they は何を指していますか。本文中の英語で答えなさい。　　　　　　（7点）

_____

4. 下線部(3)とほぼ同じ意味の語を本文中から抜き出しなさい。　　　　　　　　　　（6点）

   (　　　　　　　　　)

5. 下線部(4)は具体的に何のことですか。本文中の英語で答えなさい。　　　　　　　（7点）

_____

6. 下線部(5)について、特に the group call においてはどのようなことが言えますか。日本語で説明

   しなさい。　　　　　　　　　　　　　　　　　　　　　　　　　　　　　　　　（8点）

_____

7. **全体把握** 本文の内容と合っているものにはT、合っていないものにはFと答えなさい。（各2点）

   (ア) Remote meetings are completely different from online meetings.　（　　　　　）

   (イ) At any meeting, people get together, present ideas and make some decisions.

                                                （　　　　　）

   (ウ) People attending remote meetings are in the same room.　（　　　　　）

   (エ) Remote meetings require cellphones, computers and projectors.　（　　　　　）

   (オ) The number of participants in the group call should be 10 or less.

                                                （　　　　　）

Lesson 8 仮定法

1 次の各文がほぼ同じ意味になるように、(　)内に適語を補いなさい。　　　　(各3点)

1. I'm not happy because I don't have a car.

   I (　　　　　) (　　　　　　　　) happy if I (　　　　　　) a car.

2. That book is too expensive, so I'm not going to buy it.

   If that book (　　　　　) not so expensive, I (　　　　　) (　　　　　) it.

3. I can't meet you tomorrow because I have to work late.

   I (　　　　　) (　　　　　　　　) you tomorrow if I (　　　　　　) have to work late.

2 例にならって、次の各文を I wish＋仮定法の文に書きかえなさい。　　　　(各4点)

例：I'm sorry that I can't play the piano. → I wish I could play the piano.

1. I'm sorry that I don't know her email address.

   _____

2. I'm sorry that I can't go to his birthday party.

   _____

3. I'm sorry that I'm not good at singing a song.

   _____

3 (　)内に与えられた語句を並べかえて、英文を完成しなさい。　　　　(各4点)

1. もっとお金があれば、新しいコンピュータを買えるのに。

   (had / I / if / money / more), I could buy a new computer.

   _____

2. 私がもう少し若かったら、富士山に登るのですが。

   I would climb Mt. Fuji if (a little / I / were / younger).

   _____

3. 世界に銃がなければなあ。

   (any guns / I / there / weren't / wish) in the world.

   _____

　CAN-DO List　☐　〈知識・技能〉仮定法過去、I wish＋仮定法の文を適切に活用することができる。

4 長めの対話を一つ聞き、問いの答えとして最も適当なものを一つずつ選びなさい。 （各5点）

1. How long do German people usually take holidays?

① Less than 14 days.　　　　② Two weeks.

③ 30 days.　　　　　　　　④ 60 days.

2. Why can German and French people take long vacations?

① Because their boss tells them to do so.　② Because they are sharing their work.

③ Because they are lazy.　　　　　　　④ Because they don't have too much work.

Rapid Reading 目標 ➡ 5分 テーマ 休暇  共通テスト

5 グラフを読み取って、問いに対する答えとして最も適当なものを一つずつ選びなさい。（各5点）

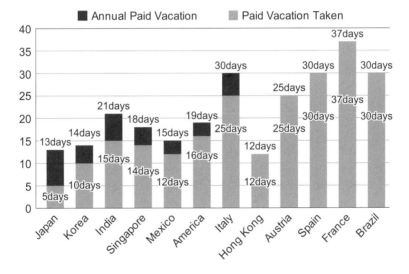

Annual Paid Vacation：年間有給休暇　　　Paid Vacation Taken：取得された有給休暇

1. Which countries take less than 80 percent of their paid vacation?

① Singapore, India, Korea, Japan.　② Brazil, France, Spain, Austria.

③ Hong Kong, Italy, America, Mexico.　④ America, Mexico, Singapore, India.

2. How much paid vacation do Japanese people take every year?

① Double their annual paid vacation.

② Half of their annual paid vacation.

③ Less than half of their annual paid vacation.

④ More than half of their annual paid vacation.

Reading　目標 ➡ 20分　　　文法項目 仮定法過去　テーマ 休暇　🔊))) 23

速読問題 次の英文を2.5分で読んで、1. の問いに答えなさい。

　How often does your father or mother take *paid vacation? Japanese workers *on average take only five paid vacation days a year, only 38 percent of the 13 days they can take. Workers in other countries take many more; for example, France 100 percent, Hong Kong 100 percent, the U.S. 83 percent, and Korea 70 percent. *That is 37 days, 12
5 days, 16 days, and 10 days, *respectively.

　Do Japanese like working so much or are they just too busy? The *survey shows that they feel they cannot *afford to take vacation and that they are afraid their *colleagues would not like them to take vacation. (1)This is a very unique reason for not taking paid vacation. In Germany, there is a law called (2)the "Holiday Law." Under
10 this law every worker has to take about four weeks of vacation a year. Two of these weeks must be *consecutive. What a big difference! (3)Maybe Japan should make a similar law.

(160 words)

---

¹ paid vacation：有給休暇　　¹ on average：平均して　　⁴ That is：すなわち
⁵ respectively [rɪspéktɪvli]：(述べられた順に) それぞれ　　⁶ survey [sə́ːrveɪ]：調査
⁷ afford [əfɔ́ːrd] to ～：～する余裕がある　　⁸ colleague [ká(ː)liːg]：同僚
¹¹ consecutive [kənsékjətɪv]：連続した

---

1. この英文で主に述べられているものを、次のa.～d.から選びなさい。　　　　（5点）

　a. 先進諸国の有給休暇制度　　　　　　　b. ドイツの「休暇法」

　c. 有給休暇の利用が進まない日本　　　　d. 労働者の権利としての有給休暇

　CAN-DO List ☐ 🧠 〈知識・技能〉仮定法過去について理解できる。
☐ 💭 〈思考力・判断力・表現力〉各国の有給休暇の利用状況について的確に理解できる。

精 読問題 もう一度英文を読んで、次の問いに答えなさい。

2. 第1パラグラフを参考にして、空欄（A）～（E）を英語で補いなさい。　　　（各3点）

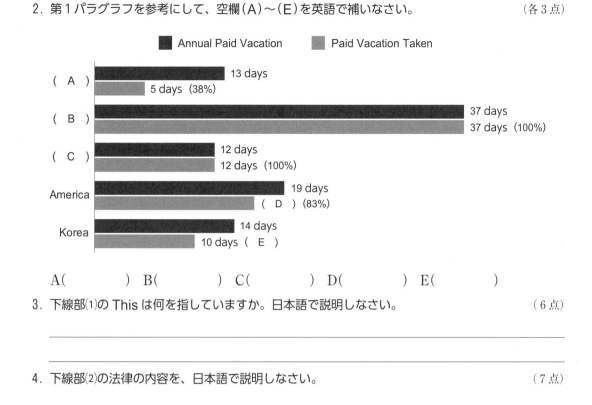

A(　　　　)　B(　　　　)　C(　　　　)　D(　　　　)　E(　　　　)

3. 下線部(1)の This は何を指していますか。日本語で説明しなさい。　　　（6点）

_____

_____

4. 下線部(2)の法律の内容を、日本語で説明しなさい。　　　（7点）

_____

_____

5. 文法 下線部(3)に関連して、「もし日本に『休暇法』があれば、日本人はもっと有給休暇をたくさんとるだろうに。」という文になるように、次の文の空所に適語を補いなさい。　　　（4点）

If there (　　　　　　　　) the "Holiday Law" in Japan, Japanese (　　　　　　　　)
(　　　　　　　　) more paid vacation days.

6. 全体把握 本文の内容と合っているものにはT、合っていないものにはFと答えなさい。（各2点）

(ア) Only 30 percent of the Japanese workers take paid vacation.　　　（　　　）

(イ) Workers in Hong Kong take as many paid vacation days as workers in France.

（　　　）

(ウ) For Japanese workers, working outside the home is more important than enjoying their family life.　　　（　　　）

(エ) Many Japanese workers don't want to take paid vacation.　The reason for this is related to their human relations.　　　（　　　）

(オ) In Germany, the government encourages the people to take vacation. (　　　)

Lesson 9 受動態

Grammar 目標 ➡ 7分

1 次の各文の（　）内に入れるのに最も適当なものを選び、記号を補いなさい。 （各2点）

1. Soccer (　　　　　) in most countries in the world.

   a. is played 　　　b. is playing 　　　c. plays

2. My bicycle (　　　　) a few days ago.

   a. stole 　　　b. was stealing 　　　c. was stolen

3. These words (　　　　) in Scotland.

   a. do not use 　　　b. are not used 　　　c. are not using

4. Why (　　　　) to the wrong address?

   a. did the letter send 　　　b. was the letter sending 　　　c. was the letter sent

2 （　）内に適語を補って、次の各文を受動態の文に書きかえなさい。 （各2点）

1. They sell stamps in convenience stores.

   Stamps (　　　　　) (　　　　　) in convenience stores.

2. A dog bit my brother last week.

   My brother (　　　　　) (　　　　　) by a dog last week.

3. He did not lock the door of his room.

   The door of his room (　　　　　) (　　　　　) locked.

4. Do you clean these rooms every day?

   (　　　　　) these rooms (　　　　　) every day?

Writing 目標 ➡ 5分

3 （　）内に適語を補って、英文を完成しなさい。 （各4点）

1. この町はいつも清潔です。通りは毎日掃除されます。

   This town is always clean. The streets (　　　　　) (　　　　　) every day.

2. イヌはしばしば人間の最良の友と呼ばれています。

   Dogs (　　　　　) often (　　　　　) human's best friends.

3. チョークは、ホワイトボードには使われません。

   A piece of chalk (　　　　　) (　　　　　) (　　　　　) on a whiteboard.

4. その国では英語が話されていますか。

   (　　　　　) (　　　　　) (　　　　　) in that country?

CAN-DO List 　□ 🔍 〈知識・技能〉受動態の基本形の文を適切に活用することができる。

Listening

目標 ➡ 3分　　テーマ　環境（水問題）　英検®　 24〜25

4 それぞれのイラストについて対話を聞き、最後の発言に対する相手の応答として最も適当なものを一つずつ選びなさい。　（各5点）

1.

① We are always short of water.
② We can use most of the salt water.
③ We can use only 0.01%.
④ We can use over 90%.

2.

① He gives 100,000 yen every game.
② He is a pitcher of Major League Baseball.
③ He knew when he won a game.
④ He started it in 2007.

Rapid Reading

目標 ➡ 5分　　テーマ　環境（水問題）　共通テスト

5 グラフを読み取って、問いに対する答えとして最も適当なものを一つずつ選びなさい。（各5点）

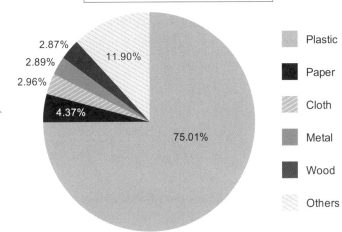

Marine Garbage on Beaches

Plastic 75.01%
Others 11.90%
4.37%
2.96%
2.89%
2.87%

Plastic / Paper / Cloth / Metal / Wood / Others

1. What represents the highest percentage of garbage?

① Plastic.　② Paper.　③ Metal.　④ Others.

2. Which garbage is seen the most on beaches?

① Broken bicycles.　② PET bottles.　③ Empty glass jars.　④ Animal bones.

Reading 目標➡20分 | 文法項目 受動態 | テーマ 環境（水問題） | ◀)) 26

速**読問題** 次の英文を2.5分で読んで、1. の問いに答えなさい。

Over 70 percent of planet Earth is covered (1)<u>with</u> saltwater oceans and seas. *Amazingly, 97 percent of the water on our planet is in the oceans.   There are a lot more living things in the oceans than on land.   That is why we *consume billions of tons of seafood, *seaweed and salt from the oceans and seas every year.   It is hard to
5 imagine life without oceans.

   *Unfortunately, we now face a new problem : dead zones.   In dead zones fish and plants cannot live because there is not enough *oxygen.   (2)<u>Dead zones are becoming a bigger problem every year.</u>   There are now more than 400 dead zones around the world.   Some scientists think dead zones *threaten human *development.

10 Most dead zones are (3)<u>caused by human activity</u>.   One main cause is the *fertilizers used in farming which get *washed off the land and (4)<u>go out to sea</u>.   Industrial waste from factories and *mines are also a cause.   Another cause is *sewage and *chemicals from big cities.   Then, of course, 30 percent of the *carbon dioxide that humans create by burning fossil fuels also *ends up in the oceans.

(187 words)

---

² amazingly [əméɪzɪŋli]：驚くべきことに　　³ consume [kənsjúːm]：…を消費する、…を食べる
⁴ seaweed [síːwìːd]：海藻　　⁶ unfortunately [ʌnfɔːrtʃ(ə)nətli]：不運にも、あいにく
⁷ oxygen [ɑ́(ː)ksɪdʒ(ə)n]：酸素　　⁹ threaten [θrét(ə)n]：…をおどす、…の脅威となる
⁹ development [dɪvéləpmənt]：発達、発展　　¹⁰ fertilizer [fɚːrt(ə)làɪzər]：肥料
¹¹ wash A off B：AをBから洗い流す　　¹² mine [máɪn]：鉱山　　¹² sewage [súː(ː)ɪdʒ]：下水
¹² chemical [kémɪk(ə)l]：化学物質　　¹³ carbon dioxide [kɑ́ːrb(ə)n daɪɑ́(ː)ksaɪd]：二酸化炭素
¹⁴ end up in ...：最後には…に入ることになる

| CAN-DO List | □ 〈知識・技能〉受動態について理解できる。
□ 〈思考力・判断力・表現力〉「死の海域」の問題について的確に理解できる。

1. この英文で主に述べられているものを、次の a.～d. から選びなさい。　　　　（5点）

　　a. 急増する「死の海域」とその原因

　　b. 人類の生存を支えている海

　　c. 地球における海の役割

　　d. 人間がもたらすさまざまな環境汚染

精 読問題 もう一度英文を読んで、次の問いに答えなさい。

2. 下線部(1)の with に最も近い意味・用法の with を含む文を、次の a.～d. から選びなさい。（5点）

　　a. Children filled the hole <u>with</u> sand.

　　b. I will go <u>with</u> you to the zoo.

　　c. She was shaking <u>with</u> fear.

　　d. They want to live in a house <u>with</u> a garden.

3. 下線部(2)の理由を、日本語で説明しなさい。　　　　（7点）

_____

_____

4. 文法 下線部(3)について、「死の海域」の原因となっているものを英語で4つ列挙しなさい。

（各3点）

_____

_____

_____

_____

5. 下線部(4)とほぼ同じ内容を表している箇所を本文中から5語で抜き出しなさい。　　　　（7点）

_____

6. 全体把握 本文の内容と合っているものにはT、合っていないものにはFと答えなさい。（各2点）

　　(ア) 地球上の水のうち真水は3パーセント未満である。　　　　　　　　　（　　　　）

　　(イ) 人類の食糧は、そのほとんどを海産物に依存している。　　　　　　（　　　　）

　　(ウ)「死の海域」では、酸素不足のために生物が生息できない。　　　　（　　　　）

　　(エ)「死の海域」は、自然現象である。　　　　　　　　　　　　　　　　（　　　　）

　　(オ) 大都市から排出される下水や化学物質が、「死の海域」を生み出す最大の原因である。

　　　　　　　　　　　　　　　　　　　　　　　　　　　　　　　　　　（　　　　）

　　(カ) 化石燃料の消費から生じる二酸化炭素も、そのほとんどが最終的には海に蓄積される。

　　　　　　　　　　　　　　　　　　　　　　　　　　　　　　　　　　（　　　　）

Lesson 10 to-不定詞①

Grammar 目標 ➡ 7分

1 ___ に下記の語群から適語を選び、to-不定詞（to＋動詞の原形）にして補いなさい。 （各2点）

1. I'm tired. I want _____ to bed.

2. Don't forget _____ us a postcard when you're on vacation.

3. Her dream was _____ around the world.

4. People must have clean water _____.

5. He had no money and no friend _____ him.

6. This machine is very simple. It is easy _____ it.

7. Hello, Jane. It is nice _____ you. How are you?

【drink / go / help / send /see / travel / use】

2 （　　）内に、右のa.～e.から適当なものを選び、記号を補いなさい。 （各2点）

1. Amy went to the airport （　　　　　）.　　a. to get your letter last week

2. I turned on the television （　　　　　）.　　b. to hear that your mother is sick

3. He worked hard （　　　　）.　　c. to make a lot of money

4. We were glad （　　　　）.　　d. to meet her friend

5. I'm sorry （　　　　）.　　e. to watch the news

Writing 目標 ➡ 3分

3 （　　）内に与えられた語句を並べかえて、英文を完成しなさい。 （各4点）

1. 今夜は何をしたいですか。

   What (do / do / to / want / you) tonight?

   _____

2. メアリーは、結婚式に着ていく新しいドレスを買いました。

   Mary bought (a new dress / the wedding / to / to / wear).

   _____

3. 成功するためには、いっしょうけんめい働くことが必要である。

   It is necessary (hard / succeed / to / to / work).

   _____

CAN-DO List □ 〈知識・技能〉to-不定詞（名詞用法、形容詞用法、副詞用法）の文を適切に活用することができる。

4 長めの対話を一つ聞き、問いの答えとして最も適当なものを一つずつ選びなさい。 (各5点)

1. When does the woman read the newspaper?

　① Before going to bed.　　② Before leaving home.

　③ While preparing breakfast.　　④ While going to her work.

2. Who likes the digital versions of newspapers the most?

　① Most men.　　② The people in a crowded train.

　③ The people under 20 years of age.　　④ The people in their 20s.

Rapid Reading 目標 ➡ 5分 テーマ 新聞 英検®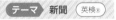

5 (1)・(2)に入れるのに最も適当なものを一つずつ選びなさい。 (各5点)

　The Sunday paper is a great American tradition.　Every city has a Sunday paper.　In a big city, it's about five times the size of the daily paper.　*Besides the usual *politics, business, and sports, you can find *human interest stories, book and movie *reviews, star interviews, almost (　1　).　And the comics are great.　While you just get one page of black and white comics in the daily paper, on Sunday there's a whole *section, and they're in color.　In fact there are lots of *separate sections for different topics, so everyone in the family (　2　).

---

²besides [bɪsáɪdz]：…に加えて　　²politics [pá(:)lətɪks]：政治
³human interest stories：読者の興味をそそる三面記事　　³review [rɪvjúː]：論評
⁵section [sékʃ(ə)n]：(新聞の数ページにわたる)…欄　　⁶separate [sép(ə)rət]：別個の

1.　① anybody　　② anything

　　③ everywhere　　④ nothing

2.　① can read at the same time

　　② can read the same section at different times

　　③ can talk about the same topic

　　④ can talk about many different topics

Reading

目標 ➡ 20分　　文法項目 to-不定詞　　テーマ 新聞　　🔊 28

速 読問題 次の英文を2.5分で読んで、1. の問いに答えなさい。

Would you like to try (1)to read a book that is 140 pages long every day?　Many

Japanese are surprised (2)to learn how long some American newspapers are.　They are

not always 140 pages long, but they are usually at least 50 pages long.　On Sundays,

some big city newspapers have hundreds of pages and *weigh almost a kilogram.

5　(3)Of course, not everything in such a newspaper is news.　There are lots of sections

about books, movies, travel, computers and hobbies, as well as star interviews and

comics in color.　There are also many *advertisements, of course, but a lot of people

find the advertisements very entertaining.　Of course, the newspapers have a lot of

news, too.

10　You may be surprised to find that (4)such large newspapers are (5)very cheap.　They

are much cheaper than a newspaper in Japan.　A large, heavy Sunday *edition of a

newspaper in a big city may only cost about 350 yen, but it is 20 times bigger than the

Sunday edition of a Japanese newspaper.　　　　　　　　　　　　　　　(171 words)

---

⁴ weigh [wéɪ]：重さが…である　　⁷ advertisement [ædvərtáɪzmənt]：広告
¹¹ edition [ɪdíʃ(ə)n]：(新聞の)…版

　CAN-DO List　☐ 🔍 〈知識・技能〉to-不定詞について理解できる。
☐ 💭 〈思考力・判断力・表現力〉アメリカの新聞の特徴について的確に理解できる。

1. この英文で主に述べられているものを、次の a.〜d. から選びなさい。 (5点)

    a. Americans —— great readers of newspapers.

    b. Big city newspapers in America.

    c. Newspapers in the world.

    d. Sunday editions of American newspapers.

精 読問題 もう一度英文を読んで、次の問いに答えなさい。

2. **文法** 下線部(1)、(2)の to-不定詞と同じ用法の to-不定詞を含む文を、それぞれ次の a.〜d. から選びなさい。 (各2点)

    a. It is cold.　Don't forget to wear your coat.

    b. Would you like something to drink?

    c. Children go to school to learn things.

    d. She was sorry to miss the beginning of the concert.

    (1) (　　　　　)　(2) (　　　　　)

3. 下線部(3)について、ニュース以外に新聞にはどのようなものが載っていますか。日本語で列挙しなさい。 (7点)

4. 下線部(4)について、その大きさを日本の新聞と比較して説明した箇所を本文中から抜き出しなさい。 (8点)

5. 下線部(5)の具体的な内容を、日本語で説明しなさい。 (8点)

6. **全体把握** 本文の内容と合っているものにはT、合っていないものにはFと答えなさい。 (各2点)

    (ア) American people read a book that is 140 pages long every day.　(　　　　　)

    (イ) American newspapers are sometimes 140 pages long.　(　　　　　)

    (ウ) American newspapers are usually 50 pages longer than Japanese ones.

    (　　　　　)

    (エ) Everything in Sunday papers is news.　(　　　　　)

    (オ) A lot of people enjoy the advertisements in Sunday papers.　(　　　　　)

    (カ) Sunday papers are cheaper than daily papers.　(　　　　　)

Lesson 11 to-不定詞②

Grammar 目標 ➡ 7分

1 次の各文がほぼ同じ意味になるように、( )内に適語を補いなさい。 (各3点)

1. She said to him, "Leave the room at once."

   She ( ) him to leave the room at once.

2. She said to him, "Please help me."

   She ( ) him to help ( ).

3. Paul was sick, so I said to him, "You should see a doctor."

   Paul was sick, so I advised ( ) ( ) ( ) a doctor.

4. I shared his umbrella with him.

   He let ( ) ( ) his umbrella with him.

2 次の日本文の意味になるように、( )内に下記の語群から適語を選んで補いなさい。(各3点)

1. 私は何と言ったらいいのかわかりませんでした。

   I didn't know ( ) to ( ).

2. この洗濯機の使い方を教えてくれませんか。

   Can you show me ( ) to ( ) this washing machine?

3. どこに車を止めればいいのか教えてくれませんか。

   Can you tell me ( ) to ( ) the car?

【how / what / where / park / say / use】

Writing 目標 ➡ 3分

3 ( )内に与えられた語句を並べかえて、英文を完成しなさい。 (各4点)

1. 私は、あなたにいっしょに来てもらいたい。

   I want (come / me / to / with / you).

   _____

2. これらのいすを運ぶのを手伝ってくれませんか。

   Will you (carry / help / me / these chairs)?

   _____

3. ジェフに聞いてごらん。どうしたらいいか教えてくれるよ。

   Ask Jeff. He'll (do / tell / to / what / you).

   _____

CAN-DO List □ 〈知識・技能〉S＋V＋O＋to-不定詞[原形不定詞]、疑問詞＋to-不定詞の文を適切に活用することができる。

4 英文と質問を聞き、その答えとして最も適当なものを一つずつ選びなさい。　(各5点)

1. ① We turn on an air-conditioner for each room.

   ② We turn on all air-conditioners for only 2 hours.

   ③ We stop using all air-conditioners.

   ④ We use fewer air-conditioners.

2. ① 2%　　　② 83%　　　③ 85%　　　④ 87%

Rapid Reading 目標 ➡ 5分　　テーマ 環境 英検®

5 (1)・(2)に入れるのに最も適当なものを一つずつ選びなさい。　(各5点)

Did you know that the Japanese word *mottainai* has become an English word? *Mottainai* was *originally a *Buddhist term which meant the misuse of something *sacred or respected.　Today, many people use this word when they don't want others (1).　*Wangari Maathai used the word *mottainai* to encourage the world to take part in the 3R campaign (Reduce waste, Re-use resources, and Recycle what we can). The word *mottainai* is now used as a slogan for the ecological movement, and is inspiring people all over the world to stand up together (2).

---

²originally [ərídʒ(ə)n(ə)li]：もとは、元来　　²Buddhist term：仏教用語
³sacred [séɪkrɪd]：神聖な　　⁴Wangari Maathai：ワンガリ・マータイ (1940–2011) ケニアの環境保護運動家

---

1. ① to eat too much

   ② to repeat a mistake

   ③ to take some risks

   ④ to waste things

2. ① to make governments change their policies

   ② to protect endangered species

   ③ to solve environmental problems

   ④ to stop the destruction of the rainforests

Reading　目標➡20分　文法項目 S＋V＋O＋to-不定詞　テーマ 環境　🔊 31

速読問題 次の英文を2.5分で読んで、1. の問いに答えなさい。

Mottainai is a Japanese word. If you buy a new notebook before finishing your old notebook, someone in your family will say, "*Mottainai*." It means "Wait. You can still use that. You don't have to buy another one."

Now *mottainai* has become a key word for an *ecology campaign. Who began to use
5 this Japanese word for the campaign? *A Kenyan woman did. She worried about the forests in her country and wanted to save them, so she began *the Green Belt Movement in 1977. Since then, she and the other members have planted 30,000,000 trees or more. (1)She is known as "the tree woman of Kenya." For her hard work she got the Nobel Peace Prize in 2004. This news made her very famous around the world.

10 Some Japanese people who heard the news asked her to come to Japan. (2)In 2005 she visited Japan. (3)During her stay in Japan something important happened to her. She heard the Japanese word *mottainai*. She understood that the word had an important idea for helping the earth. (4)She wanted many people around the world to know the word *mottainai*, so she began to use it everywhere in her speeches. *Thanks to this
15 Kenyan woman, many Japanese people have realized that the idea behind *mottainai* is wonderful.

(214 words)

---

4 ecology campaign：環境保護運動　　5 a Kenyan woman：Wangari Maathai のこと
6 the Green Belt Movement：グリーンベルト運動(森林保護のための植林活動)
14 thanks to ...：…のおかげで

　CAN-DO List　□ 🔧 〈知識・技能〉S＋V＋O＋to-不定詞について理解できる。
　　　　　　　　□ 💡 〈思考力・判断力・表現力〉「もったいない」を唱えたあるケニア人女性について的確に理解できる。

1. この英文のタイトルとして最も適当なものを、次の a.～ d.から選びなさい。　　　　　（5点）

 a. ものを大事に使わないのは「もったいない」

 b. 植林運動と「もったいない」

 c. 発展途上国の生活を守る「もったいない」

 d. 地球環境を守る「もったいない」

精 読問題 もう一度英文を読んで、次の問いに答えなさい。

2. 下線部(1)の理由を、日本語で説明しなさい。　　　　　（8点）

_____

_____

3. 文法 下線部(2)のきっかけとなったことは何ですか。日本語で説明しなさい。　　　　　（7点）

_____

_____

4. 下線部(3)の something important とは具体的には何ですか。日本語で説明しなさい。　　　　　（7点）

_____

5. 文法 下線部(4)の理由を日本語で説明しなさい。　　　　　（8点）

_____

_____

6. 全体把握 本文に続く次の英文の空所に入れるのに最も適当なものを、下の a.～ f.のうちから一つずつ選びなさい。ただし、文頭に来るべき語も小文字で示しています。　　　　　（各2点）

 What can we do for the earth?　Some of you may think that it is very difficult to plant many trees like that Kenyan woman did.　But don't worry.　There are many other things you can do around you.　Just remember the idea of *mottainai* and do something. For example, (　　ア　　) off the TV when you are not watching it.　(　　イ　　) using too much water when you (　　ウ　　) your hands.　(　　エ　　) a bag with you when you (　　オ　　) shopping.　You will (　　カ　　) that these things are not so difficult to do.

 a. go b. find c. stop d. take e. turn f. wash

 (ア) (　　　　　)　(イ) (　　　　　)　(ウ) (　　　　　)　(エ) (　　　　　)

 (オ) (　　　　　)　(カ) (　　　　　)

Lesson 12 動名詞

1 次の各文がほぼ同じ意味になるように、（　　　）内に適語を補いなさい。　　（各2点）

1. It isn't easy to play the violin.

　（　　　　　　　　）the violin isn't easy.

2. Bob's hobby is to collect stamps.

　Bob's hobby is（　　　　　　　　）stamps.

3. Do you like to travel by train?

　Do you like（　　　　　　　　）by train?

4. She started to play the piano when she was six.

　She started（　　　　　　　　）the piano when she was six.

5. When did you begin to learn English?

　When did you begin（　　　　　　　　）English?

2 （　　　）内に下記の語群から適語を選び、動名詞にして補いなさい。　　（各2点）

1. （　　　　　　　　）a walk every day is good for your health.

2. One of my bad habits is（　　　　　　）my nails.

3. I'm not in a hurry.　I don't mind（　　　　　　）.

4. He was angry with the child for（　　　　　　）the cat.

5. Can you touch your toes without（　　　　　　）your knees?

　【bend / bite / kick / take / wait】

3 （　　　）内に適語を補って、英文を完成しなさい。　　（各3点）

1. その老人の最大の楽しみは、イヌを連れて公園を散歩することでした。

　The old man's great pleasure was（　　　　　　）in the park（　　　　　　）his dog.

2. たいていの女性は、ウィンドーショッピングを楽しみます。

　Most women enjoy（　　　　　　）at the goods in shop windows.

3. そんなに騒がしくするのはやめてください。

　Please stop（　　　　　　）so much noise.

4. 彼は、さよならも言わないで部屋を出て行きました。

　He went out of the room（　　　　　　）（　　　　　　）good-bye.

CAN-DO List □ 🔊 〈知識・技能〉動名詞の基本用法の文を適切に活用することができる。

Listening

目標 → 5分   テーマ 自転車   32

4 長めの英文を聞き、問いの答えとして最も適当なものを一つずつ選びなさい。   (各5点)

1. What percentage of the accidents came from bikes this year?

① 2%   ② 10%

③ 12%   ④ 20%

2. Which of the following is a dangerous thing to do when you ride a bike?

① To think of a bike as a vehicle.   ② To cover your head.

③ To use earphones.   ④ To use a car horn.

Rapid Reading

目標 → 5分   テーマ 自転車 英検®

5 （1）・（2）に入れるのに最も適当なものを一つずつ選びなさい。   (各5点)

　　The first real bicycle was made in Scotland. It was built in 1839 by a man named Macmillan. His bicycle had two *wheels like a *modern bicycle. But （　1　）. It was heavier because it was made of wood and *iron. It did not have *rubber tires like a modern bicycle. *Instead, it had wooden wheels. This made it very uncomfortable on *bumpy roads. But Macmillan was lucky about one thing: （　2　）!

> ²wheel [(h)wíːl]：車輪　　²modern [mά(ː)dərn]：現代の、今日の　　³iron [áɪərn]：鉄
> ³rubber [rʌ́bər]：ゴムの　　⁴instead [ɪnstéd]：その代わりに　　⁵bumpy [bʌ́mpi]：でこぼこの

1. ① it was just as easy to ride   ② it was just as difficult to ride

③ it was much easier to ride   ④ it was much more difficult to ride

2. ① his bicycles did not get a flat tire

② his bicycles did not have to find a place to park

③ his bicycles did not have brakes

④ his bicycles did not cause any pollution

Reading

目標 ➡ 20分　　　文法項目　動名詞　テーマ　自転車　🔊 33

速読問題 次の英文を2.5分で読んで、1. の問いに答えなさい。

Many people enjoy cycling in Holland, and bicycles are very popular there.

Almost everyone in Holland has a bicycle.　Some people have more than one. There are about 17,000,000 bicycles in Holland, and the number of people there is about 16,000,000.　This is the highest "*bicycle density" in the world.

5　(1)Why are bicycles so popular in Holland?　(2)Because it is very easy to ride a bicycle there.　Holland is a very flat country, and it doesn't rain a lot.

In Holland, people are worried about environmental problems.　(3)The government of Holland wants more people to use bicycles in place of cars because riding a bicycle is healthy and also friendly to the environment.

10　Now Holland has good and safe roads for bicycles only.　The total *length of all (4)these roads is about 18,000 km.　People can borrow bicycles in some cities.

(5)People in Holland use bicycles for many *purposes.　Young people go on picnics by bicycle.　Old people enjoy cycling in parks for their health.　Many people go shopping by bicycle.　A lot of people visit famous places for *sightseeing by bicycle.

15　Using bicycles helps to save the earth, and it also keeps us healthy.　Why don't you go cycling, too?

(201 words)

---

⁴bicycle density：自転車の普及率　　¹⁰length [léŋ(k)θ]：長さ　　¹²purpose [pə́ːrpəs]：目的
¹⁴sightseeing [sáɪtsìːɪŋ]：観光

| **CAN-DO List** | ☐ 🔍 〈知識・技能〉動名詞について理解できる。
☐ 💡 〈思考力・判断力・表現力〉オランダの自転車普及率が高い理由について的確に理解できる。

1. この英文のタイトルとして最も適当なものを、次の a.～ d. から選びなさい。　　　　（5点）

　　a．オランダ人の環境意識

　　b．オランダ人の健康志向

　　c．オランダの交通事情

　　d．オランダ人と自転車

精 読問題 もう一度英文を読んで、次の問いに答えなさい。

2. 下線部(1)の理由を、日本語で具体的に説明しなさい。　　　　（7点）

_____

_____

3. 文法 下線部(2)、(3)とそれぞれ同じ意味になるように、次の各文の空所に適語を補いなさい。

　　　　　　　　　　　　　　　　　　　　　　　　　　　　　　　　　　　（各4点）

　　(2) Because (　　　　　　) (　　　　　　) (　　　　　　) there is very easy.

　　(3) The government of Holland hopes that more people (　　　　　) bicycles in

　　　　place of cars because (　　　　　) (　　　　　) a bicycle is healthy and also

　　　　friendly to the environment.

4. 下線部(4)の具体的な内容を、日本語で説明しなさい。　　　　（8点）

_____

5. 下線部(5)の many purposes を、具体的に日本語で説明しなさい。　　　　（8点）

_____

_____

6. 全体把握 本文の内容と合っているものにはＴ、合っていないものにはＦと答えなさい。（各2点）

　　(ア) Most of the people in Holland have two bicycles.　　　　（　　　　）

　　(イ) The number of bicycles is larger than that of people in Holland.　　（　　　　）

　　(ウ) Holland is very flat so people are interested in driving cars.　　（　　　　）

　　(エ) There are not enough roads for cars in Holland.　　　　（　　　　）

　　(オ) Bicycle racing is the most popular sport in Holland.　　　　（　　　　）

　　(カ) There are many people who use bicycles for sightseeing in Holland.　（　　　　）

Lesson 13 分詞

Grammar　目標 ➡ 7分

1 （　）内に下記の語群から適語を選び、現在分詞か過去分詞にして補いなさい。　　　（各2点）

1. Jimmy looked at the (　　　　　　) hamster and asked, "Is it alive?"

2. We don't have much money, so we decided to buy a (　　　　　) car.

3. The firefighter entered the (　　　　　) building to save the children inside.

4. A bird with a (　　　　　) wing cannot fly.

　【break / burn / sleep / use】

2 例にならって、文を作りなさい。　　　（各3点）

　　例：Do you know the girl (She is dancing with Tom.)?

　　　　→Do you know the girl dancing with Tom?

1. Who is the boy (He is sitting in the corner.)?

　_____

2. The woman (She is crossing the street.) is our English teacher.

　_____

3. What is the language (It is spoken in Holland.)?

　_____

4. The police are looking for a man (He is called "Black Tiger.").

　_____

Writing　目標 ➡ 5分

3 （　）内に与えられた語句を並べかえて、英文を完成しなさい。　　　（各4点）

1. この写真は、走行中の列車の窓から撮られました。

　This photograph was taken from (a / moving / of / the window / train).

　_____

2. バスは出勤する人々でいっぱいでした。

　The buses were full (going / of / people / to / work).

　_____

3. チーズとバターは乳製品です。

　Cheese and butter (are / from / made / milk / products).

　_____

　CAN-DO List　□　〈知識・技能〉分詞の限定用法の文を適切に活用することができる。

Listening

目標 ➡ 3分　　テーマ　海洋汚染　GTEC®　 34〜35

4 それぞれの問いについて対話を聞き、答えとして最も適当なものを一つずつ選びなさい。（各5点）

1. 男性は何を飲みますか。

2. 彼らはどこにいますか。

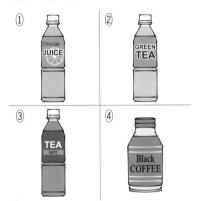

Rapid Reading

目標 ➡ 5分　　テーマ　海洋汚染　英検®

5 掲示を読み取って、問いに対する答えとして最も適当なものを一つずつ選びなさい。　（各5点）

---

*Prohibited Items at the Public Beach

Recently, citizens have *complained about the manners of some people at this beach.　We ask for your understanding *regarding the following *prohibitions.

・No smoking & no drinking of alcoholic beverages

・No throwing away waste

（Thrown away plastic bottles contribute to microplastic pollution.）

・No loud voices & no use of loudspeakers

Please *observe the above and enjoy your time on the beach safely and comfortably.

ABC City

---

¹prohibit [prouhíbət]：…を禁止する　　²complain [kəmpléɪn]：苦情を寄せる
³regarding [rɪgáːrdɪŋ]：…について　　³prohibition [pròʊəbíʃ(ə)n]：禁止事項
⁸observe [əbzáːrv]：…を遵守する

1. What is the problem for citizens?

　① Accidents at the sea.　　② Bad manners at the beach.

　③ The microplastic problem.　　④ Too much noise.

2. Which is prohibited at the beach?

　① Bringing beverages.　　② Playing with beach balls.

　③ Throwing away garbage.　　④ Using plastic products.

Reading 目標 ➡ 20分 | 文法項目 分詞の限定用法 | テーマ 海洋汚染 | 36

速 読問題 次の英文を2.5分で読んで、1．の問いに答えなさい。

Today, there are billions of tons of plastic on the Earth.　Most of (1)that has become

waste.　Unfortunately, we only recycle a small percentage of (2)the plastic.　As a result,

a huge amount of unrecycled plastic waste has ended up in our oceans.

　(3)Ocean plastic has killed millions of sea animals, from very tiny creatures to whales.

5 Some have gotten caught in plastic fishing nets or *six-pack rings.　Many more

creatures have died after eating microplastics.　Microplastics are very small rice-

sized pieces of plastic.　Scientists have found microplastics from the bottom of the

deepest oceans to ice in the Arctic Ocean.　They say (4)they have turned the world's

ocean into a (5)"plastic soup."

10　Governments, companies and consumers have started working together to solve the

plastic waste problem.　For example, in 2017, 193 countries passed the United Nations

Clean Seas agreement to end ocean plastic pollution.　Coca-Cola has announced a goal

of collecting and recycling 100 percent of its packaging by 2030.　As a consumer, what

can you do?　(168 words)

---

⁵six-pack rings：主に飲料缶を6つまとめるためのプラスチック製品

| CAN-DO List | ☐ 〈知識・技能〉分詞の限定用法について理解できる。
☐ 〈思考力・判断力・表現力〉プラスチックによる海洋汚染について的確に理解できる。

1. この英文のタイトルとして最も適当なものを、次のa.〜d.から選びなさい。　　　　（5点）

　　a. Governments, Companies and Consumers Working Together

　　b. How to Use Six-pack Rings

　　c. The Lives of Sea Animals

　　d. The Plastic Waste Problem

精 読問題 もう一度英文を読んで、次の問いに答えなさい。

2. 下線部(1)の that は何を指していますか。本文中から1語で抜き出しなさい。　　（5点）

　　（　　　　　　　）

3. 文法 下線部(2)が「使用済みのプラスチック」という意味になるように、次の文の空所に適語を補いなさい。　　　　　　　　　　　　　　　　　　　　　　　　　　　　　　　（5点）

　　the（　　　　　　　　）plastic

4. 下線部(3)について、海の動物はどのようにプラスチックによって死んでいますか。日本語で2つ簡潔に説明しなさい。　　　　　　　　　　　　　　　　　　　　　　　　　　（各5点）

　　_____

　　_____

5. 下線部(4)の they は何を指していますか。本文中から1語で抜き出しなさい。　　（5点）

　　（　　　　　　　）

6. 下線部(5)の "plastic soup" とはどういう状態ですか。日本語で説明しなさい。　（8点）

　　_____

7. 全体把握 本文の内容と合っているものにはT、合っていないものにはFと答えなさい。（各2点）

　　(ア) There are billions of tons of plastic in the sea today.　　　　　（　　　　）

　　(イ) Most of the used plastic is recycled.　　　　　　　　　　　　（　　　　）

　　(ウ) Plastic waste usually ends up on the ground.　　　　　　　　（　　　　）

　　(エ) Microplastics are affecting marine life.　　　　　　　　　　　（　　　　）

　　(オ) Many countries passed the new agreement on the plastic problem.　（　　　　）

Lesson 14 比較

Grammar 目標 ➡ 7分

1 次の各文がほぼ同じ意味になるように、（　　）内に適語を補いなさい。 （各2点）

1. Brazil is not as large as Canada.

   Canada is (　　　　　　) (　　　　　　　) Brazil.

2. The book was not as interesting as the movie.

   The movie was (　　　　　) (　　　　　　) (　　　　　　) the book.

3. The weather is not as cold today as it was yesterday.

   The weather was (　　　　　) yesterday (　　　　　) it is today.

4. He is not as old as he looks.

   He (　　　　　) older than he really (　　　　　　).

2 ＿＿＿ 内に下記の語群から適語を選び、the＋最上級にして補いなさい。 （各2点）

1. Jupiter is ＿＿＿＿＿＿＿＿＿＿ planet in the solar system.

2. We had a great room.　It was one of ＿＿＿＿＿＿＿＿＿＿ rooms in the hotel.

3. What is ＿＿＿＿＿＿＿＿＿＿ sport in your country?

4. What's ＿＿＿＿＿＿＿＿＿＿ way of getting from here to the bus station?

5. Excuse me, where is ＿＿＿＿＿＿＿＿＿＿ bank?

   【large / near / nice / popular / quick】

Writing 目標 ➡ 3分

3 （　　）内に適語を補って、英文を完成しなさい。 （各3点）

1. 今は、昼と夜の長さがほぼ同じです。

   The days are almost (　　　　　　) long (　　　　　　) the nights now.

2. 私は、あなたほどお金をもっていません。

   I don't have as (　　　　　) (　　　　　) as you do.

3. 小型車は、大型車よりも駐車がずっと容易です。

   Small cars are much (　　　　　) to park (　　　　　) big ones.

4. ロープは、長さが2フィート余った。

   The rope was two feet (　　　　　　) than we needed.

5. 私は、クラスで成績のトップグループに入りたい。

   I want to be (　　　　　) of the (　　　　　) students in the class.

CAN-DO List ☐ 〈知識・技能〉as＋原級＋as、比較級＋than、最上級の文を適切に活用することができる。

Listening 目標 ➡ 5分 テーマ 仕事 🔊 37

4 長めの英文を一つ聞き、問いの答えとして最も適当なものを一つずつ選びなさい。 (各5点)

1. Who is this announcement for?

① Company workers.   ② Customers in the restaurant.

③ Full-time staff.   ④ The president of the firm.

2. Which are part-time workers NOT allowed to do?

① Avoid working in the morning.

② Come to work three times a week.

③ Take a break for half an hour in the afternoon.

④ Work on Mondays, Wednesdays, and Fridays.

Rapid Reading 目標 ➡ 5分 テーマ 仕事 英検®

5 （1）・（2）に入れるのに最も適当なものを一つずつ選びなさい。 (各5点)

A lot of university students these days join internship programs, a kind of work experience *opportunity for students. *Interns usually do the same work as the company staff. Some of them even get paid for their work. An internship program is （ 1 ） because it gives them a chance to decide whether the job they are doing is right for them or not. Thanks to the internship programs, many students （ 2 ） when they graduate.

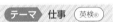

²opportunity [à(:)pərtjúːnəti]：機会   ²intern [íntəːrn]：インターン生、研修生

1. ① perfect for students

  ② suitable for universities

  ③ useful for company workers

  ④ useless for students

2. ① decide to work overseas

  ② don't have much trouble getting a job

  ③ find out that it is difficult to get a job

  ④ want to continue their study

Reading　目標 ➡ 20分　　　　　　文法項目 比較　テーマ 仕事　🔊 38

速 読問題 次の英文を2.5分で読んで、1. の問いに答えなさい。

　In a traditional company, workers spend five days a week at the office.　They often spend 30 minutes or longer traveling to and from work.　During rush hour, *traffic congestion and air pollution are often quite serious.　Teleworking (also called "telecommuting") is one way to reduce these problems.

5　Teleworkers have office jobs, but they work at home one or more days each month. By using telephones and computers with Internet access, they can do all of their regular office tasks.　(1)Many jobs, such as sales, design, and even office management, can be done from home.

　Teleworking has many benefits.　With fewer cars on the road, traffic and air quality

10 improve.　Companies save money by spending less on office space.　Also, employees who telework are (2)happier with their jobs.

　Some companies, however, are slow to accept teleworking.　They think employees need managers (3)looking over their shoulder or they won't work hard.　(4)In fact, studies show that to be far from the truth.　People actually get 25% more work done when they telework.

15　There are already more than 20 million teleworkers in Europe and the U.S.A.　Japan has more than 10 million, and Australia has about three million.　These numbers are growing as more people learn the benefits of this modern way to do a day's work.

(215 words)

2 traffic congestion：交通渋滞

58　CAN-DO List　□ 〈知識・技能〉比較について理解できる。
　　　　　　　　　　□ 〈思考力・判断力・表現力〉テレワークの利点について的確に理解できる。

1. この英文のタイトルとして最も適当なものを、次のa.～d.から選びなさい。 （5点）

　　a. A New Style of Working

　　b. Differences Between Teleworking and Telecommuting

　　c. Introducing Teleworking to Traditional Companies

　　d. Teleworking and Environmental Problems

精 読問題 もう一度英文を読んで、次の問いに答えなさい。

2. 下線部(1)について、テレワークをするために必要なものを、本文中から2つ抜き出しなさい。

（各5点）

_____

_____

3. 文法 下線部(2)は employees who telework と何を比較していますか。英語で答えなさい。

（8点）

_____

4. 下線部(3)と最も近い意味を表す表現を、次のa.～d.から選びなさい。 （6点）

　　a. giving useful advice to them

　　b. keeping an eye on them

　　c. looking at their shoulders carefully

　　d. working shoulder to shoulder with them

5. 下線部(4)は具体的にはどういうことですか。日本語で説明しなさい。 （8点）

_____

_____

6. 全体把握 本文の内容と合っているものにはT、合っていないものにはFと答えなさい。（各2点）

　　(ア) It usually takes teleworkers half an hour to get to the office. 　　　（　　　　）

　　(イ) Teleworking can help reduce air pollution. 　　　（　　　　）

　　(ウ) Teleworkers don't need to go to the office for more than a month. 　　　（　　　　）

　　(エ) Some companies don't want to let their employees work at home. 　　　（　　　　）

　　(オ) Japan has fewer teleworkers than Australia and the U.S.A. 　　　（　　　　）

Lesson **15** 関係代名詞

Grammar
Grammar　目標 ➡ 7分

1 （　　）内に、下のa.～d.から適当なものを選び、記号を補いなさい。 （各2点）

1. The woman (　　　　　) was wearing a yellow dress.

2. Jim was wearing a hat (　　　　).

3. I'm looking for a store (　　　　).

4. I don't like people (　　　　).

　　a. that buys and sells used books 　　　b. which was too big for him

　　c. who opened the door 　　　d. who always talk about themselves

2 例にならって、第2文を完成しなさい。 （各4点）

　　例：Ann took the pictures.　Did you see the pictures ...?

　　　　→Did you see the pictures Ann took?

1. We saw the movie.　The movie ... was very good.

_____

2. You bought the oranges.　How much were the oranges ...?

_____

3. We met the people at the party.　The people ... were very nice.

_____

Writing　目標 ➡ 3分

3 （　　）内に与えられた語句を並べかえて、英文を完成しなさい。 （各4点）

1. これらは、暖かい国々で育つ植物です。

　　These are (grow / in / plants / warm countries / which).

_____

2. 私を助けることができるのはあなただけです。

　　You are (can / only / person / that / the) help me.

_____

3. あの人が、私がアンのパーティーで出会った人です。

　　That is (Ann's party / at / I / met / the man).

_____

CAN-DO List □ 🔍 〈知識・技能〉関係代名詞（主格）、関係代名詞（目的格の省略）の文を適切に活用することができる。

Listening

目標 ➡ 5分　　　　　　　　　　　テーマ 夜　 39

4 長めの対話を一つ聞き、問いの答えとして最も適当なものを一つずつ選びなさい。　（各5点）

1. How long does Yuta play computer games?

① For an hour every day.　　② For three hours every day.

③ Too much and he is tired.　④ Too much to have enough sleep.

2. From their conversation, which of the following are computer games NOT good for?

① Our brains.　② Our eyes.　③ Our learning.　④ Our teamwork.

Rapid Reading

目標 ➡ 5分　　　　　　　　　　　テーマ 夜　GTEC®

5 ウェブサイトを読み取って、問いに対する答えとして最も適当なものを一つずつ選びなさい。

（各5点）

Nature *Observation Tour

You can see a sky full of stars in ABC Village.　In ABC Village, the stars can be seen shining most brightly.　You can enjoy a starry sky observation at your own pace.　There is no doubt that you will be impressed by the beautiful starry sky you can see in the *wilderness surrounded by silence.　It is popular not only for people who like stars, but also for those who like photography.

For inquiries, please contact the Daiichi Tour.

1 observation [à(:)bzərvéɪʃ(ə)n]：観察　　5 wilderness [wíldərnəs]：大自然

1. What can participants see in this tour?

① A lot of beautiful stars.　　② Local villagers.

③ Photographs of a starry sky.　④ Wild animals.

2. Who is the right kind of person to join this tour?

① A person who likes blue sky.　　② A person who likes city night view.

③ A person who likes photography.　④ A person who likes walking.

Reading

文法項目 関係代名詞　テーマ　夜　 40

目標 ➡ 20分

速読問題 次の英文を2.5分で読んで、1. の問いに答えなさい。

The tiny island of Niue is far away from any cities. *Unlike urban areas around the world, Niue *is free of light pollution. (1)Niue's skies are so dark, in fact, that the entire country has been named an International Dark Sky Place by the International Dark-Sky Association (2)(IDA).

5　*Remoteness alone contributes heavily to the island's dark environment, but the villages *are used to using special lighting that leaves the night sky *unspoiled. That *reveals the brilliant starry sky in its full glory. Villagers have changed or replaced streetlight and light in private *residences and business.

Culturally, the Dark Sky status will help protect (3)part of the island's tradition. For 10 centuries, its people have used the stars and moon cycles for navigation on the seas.

"Being a dark sky nation will help protect Niue's night skies for future generations of Niueans and visitors to the country," said Felicity Bollen, Niue Tourism CEO. Headlines about (4)the tiny Pacific country's accomplishment will increase nature tourism and attract a lot of nature lovers from around the world. When they arrive, 15 they'll be met by local guides who will help visitors find the best views of the skies above.

(194 words)

---

¹unlike [ʌnláɪk]：…と違って　　²be free of …：…がない
⁵remoteness [rɪmóʊtnəs]：(都会から)離れていること　　⁶be used to …：…に慣れている
⁶unspoiled [ʌnspɔ́ɪld]：自然なままの　　⁷reveal [rɪvíːl]：…を見せる　　⁸residence [rézɪd(ə)ns]：住宅

| **CAN-DO List** ☐ 🔍 〈知識・技能〉関係代名詞について理解できる。
☐ 〈思考力・判断力・表現力〉暗い夜空をもつニウエについて的確に理解できる。

1. この英文のタイトルとして最も適当なものを、次のa.〜d.から選びなさい。　（5点）

　　a．A Dark Night Sky on an Island

　　b．Inconvenient Life on an Island

　　c．Lights on an Island

　　d．The Environment on an Island

精 読問題 もう一度英文を読んで、次の問いに答えなさい。

2．下線部(1)の理由を2つ、日本語で説明しなさい。　（各6点）

_____

_____

3． 文法 下線部(2)について、日本語に合うように、次の文の空所を補ってIDAを説明する英文を作りなさい。　（6点）

「IDAは現在や未来の世代のために夜空を守るために働く団体です。」

IDA is a group (　　　　　　　) (　　　　　　　) to protect the night skies for present
and future generations.

4．下線部(3)の具体的な内容を日本語で説明しなさい。　（8点）

_____

5．下線部(4)の具体的な達成内容は何ですか。このパラグラフから5語で抜き出しなさい。　（7点）

_____

6． 全体把握 本文の内容と合っているものにはT、合っていないものにはFと答えなさい。（各2点）

　⑺ The nights in the city of Niue are so dark that it is dangerous to walk at night.

（　　　　　）

　⑼ Niue is known as an International Dark Sky Place.　（　　　　　）

　⑺ The people of Niue use special lighting in their private homes and workplaces.

（　　　　　）

　㈢ The people of Niue no longer use the cycles of the stars and the moon to sail the
seas.　（　　　　　）

　㈤ The dark night sky in Niue is bad for tourism.　（　　　　　）

Sources

■Rapid Reading

Lesson 6

MIKULECKY, BEATRICE S.; JEFFRIES, LINDA, MORE READING POWER, 1st Ed.,
©1996. Reprinted by permission of Pearson Education, Inc., New York, New York.

Lesson 9（グラフ）

Proportion of marine litter categories on reference beaches（OCEAN HEALTH INDEX）をもとに作成

Lesson 12

MIKULECKY, BEATRICE S., READING POWER, 1st Ed.,
©1986. Reprinted by permission of Pearson Education, Inc., New York, New York.

■Reading

Lesson 4

Reproduced by permission of Oxford University Press from Inside Reading Level 1 by Arline Burgmeier
© Oxford University Press 2012

Lesson 13

Robert Hickling / 臼倉美里, *Reading Link*, "Unit 12 What Plastics Done to Our Oceans?", Kinseido